CU00355113

This book belongs to:

TO AND FROM THE AIRPORT

Airports are usually located where there is enough flat land to allow one or more level runways to be built as well as all the other buildings and structures needed. When new airports are built, the designers also try to keep disturbance to local people to a minimum. Finally, the natural environment must also be taken into account. All this means that airports may be some distance from towns or cities, and anyone wishing to travel by air must first be able to get to the airport. Many passengers travel to the airport by car. Close to the terminal building there is usually a 'Short Stay Car Park' where parking is usually restricted to 24 hours. 'Long Stay Car Parks' are much bigger and are further from the terminal buildings. On a daily rate basis, Long Stay Car Parks are much cheaper than Short Stay Car Parks. Of course, when you are inside the terminal building, you will need to know how to find . . .

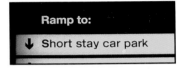

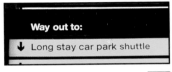

. . . the Short Stay Car Park,
I-Spy for 5

. . . and the Long Stay Car Park.
I-Spy for 5

But, as you can see, there are other ways to get to the airport . . .

. . . by train
I-Spy for 15

. . . by train and coach. This 'Railair Link' connects Heathrow Airport with British Rail at Woking.
I-Spy for 10

. . . by express coach between an airport and several other urban centres.
I-Spy for 5

2

. . . by a London Buses 'Airbus' to several stops in Central London.
I-Spy for 10

. . . by the famous London black cab.
I-Spy for 5

This 'Jetlink' coach will transfer passengers between different airports. For example, you might arrive at Luton Airport on an internal flight and then wish to transfer to Gatwick or Heathrow to fly to another country.
I-Spy for 15

Outside the terminal building, where all the buses, coaches, and taxis stop, there may be covered walkways leading from the central bus station towards the terminals.
I-Spy for 10

And in this area, you will find bus stops and timetables for . . .

AIRBUS

NCP **NCP**
Flightpath
Long Term Car Park
Courtesy Bus Stop

Hotel courtesy coaches

. . . the courtesy bus to take you to the Long Stay Car Park.
I-Spy for 5

. . . and buses to take you to one of the various hotels which are always found near airports.
I-Spy for 5

. . . the 'Airbus'.
I-Spy for 10

At a big airport, where there are several terminals, you may need to catch a bus to take you from one terminal to another.
I-Spy for 5

Minibuses can also be rented for airport use. Here is one.
I-Spy for 5

Whether you arrive by train, bus, taxi, or car, you should be able to find smartly uniformed porters who will, for a fee, take all your luggage to the check-in desk.
I-Spy for 10

But, if there is no porter available or you do not wish to pay the fee, you can use an airport baggage trolley. Look out for one of these gaps in the glass wall of the terminal where trolleys come through to the outside ready for use . . .
I-Spy for 15

. . . or a trolley park inside the terminal building.
I-Spy for 5

Of course, airport staff may also have to park their cars, and they have their own special car parks.
I-Spy for 15

And individual airlines use their own coaches to carry their staff. Here are staff coaches from two airlines.
I-Spy 10 for each of two airline coaches

If you find yourself at a big airport and you are not sure where to go, look out for one of these useful Airport Guides.
I-Spy for 10

And a Help Point will tell you which signs to follow to find what you are looking for.
I-Spy for 10

Because airports can be so big, there are many roads which are sometimes named. Look out for some unusual ones. This one would be very odd anywhere else but an airport!
I-Spy 15 for each of three unusual road names

Whether you are a passenger or not, you may need to find out the time of a flight, or if a certain passenger has arrived, or where you can hire a car. Whatever information you need, the staff at an information desk will try to help.
I-Spy for 5

Or you could try one of these multilingual information machines.
I-Spy for 15

Or even this special telephone that also functions as an emergency phone.
I-Spy for 15

And here is an emergency telephone. Notice that it is painted red and has brief instructions for you to be able to follow quickly.
I-Spy for 10

This courtesy phone can be used by airport staff to ring through to different departments without the need to use a pay phone but it can also be used by the public for internal airport calls.
I-Spy for 10

An airport terminal may offer you all kinds of facilities. These can be especially useful, if you have had to leave home in a hurry to catch your flight or if you have to wait at the airport for a long time. And, when you arrive, especially if you have set down in a different country, these services can also be very helpful.

This is a very useful service. You'll find these left luggage areas at railway stations too. You can leave your bags here, pay a fee, and you'll be given a ticket with a number matching one that is put on your luggage. To collect your bags when you return, you simply hand in your ticket.
I-Spy for 15

By the time you reach the airport, it's rather late to be getting passport photographs. On the other hand, if you know that there is one of these machines at the airport, at least you can get the photographs quickly and easily.
I-Spy for 10

At a Bureau de Change you can change money from one national currency to another, such as Pounds Sterling into US Dollars.
Above is a Thomas Cook bureau . . .
I-Spy for 5

. . . and here is another type.
I-Spy for 5

If you need to hire a car, here is a selection of companies that can arrange it for you.
I-Spy 5 for each of four different car hire companies

You can even find a Post Office at the airport — important for that last-minute letter . . !
I-Spy for 10

. . . or the person about to take a business flight may need to send or receive an urgent fax. Now he or she can use a machine and pay by credit card.
I-Spy for 15

It is very convenient to be able to pay for your car parking before you leave the terminal building so that you do not have to queue up in your car at a pay booth. Here are three different ways to pay . . .

. . . at a desk inside the terminal building.
I-Spy for **10**

. . . at a machine that will accept coins, notes, or major credit cards.
I-Spy for **5**

. . . or at a machine just for the Short Stay Car Park. For this one you must have the exact change.
I-Spy for **5**

Perhaps you're thirsty and just need a drink of water. Here is a handy drinking fountain. They are very hygienic nowadays.
I-Spy for **10**

You might need a drink, a snack, or a substantial meal. There is a variety of bars, cafés, and restaurants at most airports.
I-Spy 5 for each of two different kinds

Toilets are usually easy to find at airports. Look out for overhead signs like this. It also gives directions for departure gates, smoking area, and emergency exit.
I-Spy 5 for toilet sign

What does this sign indicate? ➡

I-Spy 5 for the sign — double with answer

And here's the way to the men's toilet as well as the baby care room. Does the toilet you've seen have facilities for the disabled?
I-Spy for 5

People from many different countries who speak different languages use airports. It is helpful if signs, such as this one for men's and women's toilets, are languageless.
I-Spy for 10

When you're travelling, you may need a wash and brush up. Here's a machine that dispenses a travel pack containing tooth-brush, toothpaste, shaving cream, razor, aftershave, comb, and shoe shine. Where would you usually find a machine like this one?

I-Spy for 5
Double with answer

↑ If just a wash is not enough, perhaps you would prefer a shower.
I-Spy for 15

And what does this ➡ languageless sign show? You have seen a sign in English already!

I-Spy 10 for the sign —
double with answer

Here is a Travel Care centre.
I-Spy for 15

Travel Care

Not every airport has one of these — a play centre to keep young children happy!
I-Spy for 20

Look out for one of these Comments Boxes. It contains a supply of forms for you to fill in with your views about the airport and its facilities. In this way, the airport authorities can get a better understanding of passengers' needs.
I-Spy for **10**

You may have noticed that at the Information Desk, there was a sign 'Meeting Point'. It is convenient to have a special place where you can arrange to meet people. Here is another kind of assembly point. Groups of travelling school children may assemble here, for example, before going to check in.
I-Spy for **10**

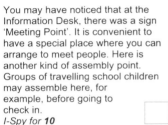

And here is an Immigration Assembly Area for incoming passengers from other countries to gather.
I-Spy for **15**

Or an arriving passenger, especially perhaps a business traveller, may be met by a driver or escort from the company he or she is visiting.
I-Spy for **10**

Some modern airports have been carefully designed so that a lot of information and equipment is centralized around supporting structures for the terminal. In this airport, this structure is known as a tree. It is fitted with lighting, air conditioning ducts, auxiliary lighting, security television camera, clock, fire hose, 13-amp electricity socket, and illuminated information boards.

I-Spy for 10

And here is a single security television camera.
I-Spy for 10

Look out for these security access machines. Only staff with the correct card keys and codes will be able to pass through doors equipped with these machines.
I-Spy for 15

If you are going to travel by air, one of the first things that you will have to do when you arrive at the airport is to check in with the airline that you are travelling with. Usually, depending on the airline, your destination, and the airport, you must do this an hour or more before your flight is due to take off. You will show your ticket and passport, your luggage will be weighed and checked in, and you will be issued with a boarding card. You may be asked questions concerned with the security of your luggage.

A sign like this one tells you where to go to check in.
I-Spy for 5

There may be a pre-check-in to speed up the check-in process.
I-Spy for 15

British Airways' famous Concorde supersonic aircraft flies only from Terminal 4 at Heathrow Airport. On this plane, Transatlantic flight times have been cut sharply.
*I-Spy for 20
Double if you see the aircraft*

CHECKING IN

Here is a small selection of well-known carriers that fly from British airports.

I-Spy 5 for each check-in desk of five different carriers

British Airways

Air UK

British Midland

Dan-Air

Aer Lingus

For some flights, especially internal routes, you may be able to buy a ticket and check in quickly and easily using an automated machine like this one.
I-Spy for **15**

17

Disabled passengers may be offered specially lowered check-in desks so that they are able to carry out the process easily from a wheelchair.
I-Spy for **15**

And provided the airport is notified in advance, it will make arrangements for disabled passengers to be escorted through from arrival at the airport to departure.
I-Spy for **15**

Or elderly people and families with lots of luggage can be transported on one of these special airport buggies.
I-Spy for **15**

A SELECTION OF SIGNS

One of the things that you'll notice when you go to any airport is just how much information you are offered by all kinds of different signs — some illuminated some not; some in English; some languageless; some overhead; and so on. Here is a selection. See how many of these you can I-Spy.

This one is outside in the airport complex.
I-Spy for 10

Look out for a sign like this one as you enter the terminal.
I-Spy for 5

These monitors give check-in information.
I-Spy for 10

This way for check-in desks numbers 41-62.
I-Spy for 5

The departure times, departure gate numbers, and any other information, such as if the flight is delayed, are shown on this board.
I-Spy for 5

A SELECTION OF SIGNS

← You'll find this baggage security notice in the check-in areas.
I-Spy for 5 ☐

➡ Here is an interesting one. It is found in terminal lounges by the seats. It shows people who have hearing difficulties where to sit to be able to hear loudspeaker announcements.
I-Spy for 15 ☐

← Lots of information on this sign! ☐
I-Spy for 5

➡ Before you pass through immigration, you might spot one of these advertisements for the duty free shopping available. ☐

I-Spy for 10

And here's a temporary sign. The airport staff call these display stands 'lollipops' . . . ☐
I-Spy for 15

. . . signs like that, or any other heavy equipment, may be transported on these buggies driven by airport porters. This one can be driven on the road and, in the airport, it makes a continuous warning noise so that passengers know it is coming. ☐
I-Spy for 15

  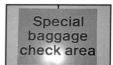

Keep a look out for these signs concerning your baggage.
I-Spy **5** for each of three

When you are meeting someone who has travelled by air, you need to know when the flight has arrived. These two kinds of arrivals monitors show the flight number, where the flight has come from, and what time it touched down.
I-Spy **5** for two different kinds of arrivals boards

And these bags have not been claimed by their owners.
I-Spy for **10**

And here are some VIPs arriving. In this case, it's a pop group. Look at the fans and journalists crowding round. What does VIP stand for?

_____

_____

I-Spy for **20**
Double with answer

It's time to go. Only passengers with valid boarding passes and, if necessary, passports can pass through this entrance.
I-Spy for 5

Here the passenger's ticket and boarding pass are being checked.
I-Spy for 10

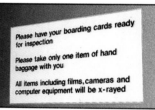

Please have your boarding cards ready for inspection

Please take only one item of hand baggage with you

All items including films, cameras and computer equipment will be x-rayed

You'll probably see a sign like this one before you go through into the flight departures area.
I-Spy for 10

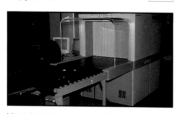

Your hand luggage will be X-rayed to make sure that you are not carrying any dangerous or illegal items. You will also be checked and this may involve a personal body search if you are carrying anything which sets off the machine.
I-Spy 10 for X-ray machine and *15 for a body search*

You might Spy a sign like this one . . .
-Spy for **15**

. . or this
-Spy for **15**

No vehicles allowed beyond this point

There are no postal facilities beyond passport control except for VAT forms

In the main departure lounge, for international flights, you will find a duty free shop. Because no duty is payable on items such as alcoholic drinks, cigarettes, and cosmetics, they are usually much cheaper than you can buy them in shops outside.
I-Spy for **10**

When your flight is called, you can follow the signs that tell you where the correct departure gate is.
-Spy for **10**

DUTY FREE SHOPPING

Departure gates
↑ Gates 1-10 ✈
Gates 12-55 ↑

You may go to the gate by moving walkway . . .
-Spy for **10**

. . which have warning signs like these two.

-Spy **5** for each

23

Or you may travel by Rapid Transit or Track Transit System to the departure gate. This is a fully automated, computerized system of cars with no drivers. The cars run on concrete rails and have rubber-tyred wheels. Electric power is picked up from a central live rail.

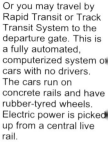

I-Spy **10** *for each of the signs leading up to the train and* **10** *more for the train*

When you arrive at the right departure gate, your boarding card will be checked again . . .
I-Spy for 5

Please wait in
this lounge
until your flight
is boarding

. . and you can go into the final departure lounge.
I-Spy for 5

Look out for special lifts like this one designed to take the hand luggage of over burdened passengers to the plane from the departure lounge.
I-Spy for 15

In the departure lounge you may see two exits, marked A and B. Exit B is for First Class and Business Class passengers and usually leads to the front of the aircraft. Exit A is for Economy Class passengers.
I-Spy for 10 if you see both

ELECTRICALLY OPERATED
SHUTTER DOOR

Barrier
Interlocked

As you board the plane, take a close look at the inside of the jetty and the aircraft's door and all the information the notices convey.
I-Spy 10 for each

At some airports, you may either have to walk across the apron to board the aircraft or you will be taken to it by a special bus. As you go, keep a look out on the tarmac: there are all kinds of interesting things to see.

Here is one of the jetties or airbridges that allows passengers to walk straight through from the departure lounge to the door of the aircraft . . .
I-Spy for **10**

. . . and here is a jetty joined to an aircraft.
I-Spy for **15**

Steps like this used to be the most common way to board an aircraft.
I-Spy for **10**

Sometimes, aircraft must be moved in or out of their parking positions by special, powerful vehicles, usually called tugs.

I-Spy 15 for each of two types

Before it can take off, an aircraft must be refuelled. At major airports, the oil companies supply fuel from large holders like these . . .
I-Spy for 15

. . . and pipework under the tarmac carries the fuel to refuelling points which look like this.
I-Spy for 15

The refuelling vehicle does not have to carry its own tanks of fuel. It is rather like a big pump on wheels.
I-Spy for 15

Pipes are connected to the refuelling point on the tarmac and to the aircraft's fuel tanks so that the refuelling vehicle can pump fuel into the plane.
I-Spy for 20

A conveyor belt like this, loading bags on to an aircraft, is usually known as a rocket.
I-Spy for **15**

So that the cabin crew on an aircraft can provide passengers with refreshments or even full meals throughout the flight, food must be loaded on to the plane by a vehicle called a high loader.
I-Spy for **15**

This vehicle, which you might see on the apron, is called a transporter and can be used to carry all kinds of things to and from aircraft.
I-Spy for **15**

Passengers' baggage is usually carried on the aircraft in metal containers like this one. These containers are known as dollies.
I-Spy for **15**

The dolly will be carried on a trailer like this . . .
I-Spy for **15**

. . . and the trailer is pulled by a tractor like this.
I-Spy for **15**

The large, sloping, metal 'fence' that you can see in this picture is called a windbreaker. Before an aircraft taxis to its take-off position, the pilot opens up the engines to full throttle for a short time. The windbreaker disperses the jet thrust so that everything behind it is not just blown away!
I-Spy for **15**

TOUCHING DOWN

After the flight is over and you have arrived at your destination, you leave the aircraft and then you must pass through passport control where your passport will be checked before you can enter the country.
I-Spy for 5

Then you go to the baggage hall to collect your luggage. A sign like this tells you which reclaim belt will deliver the luggage from your flight . . .
I-Spy for 5

. . . and one like this confirms that you are at the right reclaim belt.
I-Spy for 15

At a modern airport, the baggage reclaim hall will look
something like this.
I-Spy for 15

And you might see a
sign like this one
warning that the
conveyor is about
to start.
I-Spy for 5

The conveyor belts that carry the luggage are often
called carousels, and you wait by it until your
cases are carried along to be collected.
I-Spy for 5

33

If you are not actually entering the country but are just transferring to another flight to continue your journey elsewhere, look out for a sign like this one.
I-Spy for 10

Sometimes, it might be a clever language-less sign.
I-Spy for 15

Planning to go Green?

Only go through the Green channel if you have:
- No more than the Customs Allowances
- No goods for commercial use
- No prohibited or restricted goods

NOTHING to declare

If you are in doubt, go into the Red channel.

For goods in each colour band, you may bring in either the Duty Free or the Duty Paid allowances shown.

	DUTY FREE		DUTY PAID
	Goods obtained anywhere outside the EEC or duty and tax free within the EEC e.g. from a duty free shop.		Goods obtained duty and tax paid in the EEC.
Spirits, strong liqueurs over 22% vol	1 litre	OR	1½ litres
Fortified or sparkling wines, some liqueurs	or 2 litres		or 3 litres
Still table wine	2 litres	OR	5 litres
Perfume	60 cc/ml	OR	90 cc/ml
Toilet water	250 cc/ml	OR	375 cc/ml
Gifts, souvenirs, other goods	£32 worth but not more than 50 litres of beer 25 mechanical lighters	OR	£250 worth but not more than 50 litres of beer 25 mechanical lighters
Cigarettes	200	OR	300
Cigarillos	or 100		or 150
Cigars	or 50		or 75
Tobacco	or 250 grammes		or 400 grammes

COUNTRIES OF THE EEC
Belgium — The Irish Republic
Denmark — Luxembourg
France — The Netherlands
FR Germany — Portugal
Greece — Spain (not the Canary Islands)
Italy — The UK (not the Channel Islands)

No-one under 17 is entitled to tobacco or drinks allowances.

If you are entering the country, look out for a sign like this one that explains what goods you can legally bring in with you and what you can not.
I-Spy for 5

Then you follow the signs to the Customs Hall where your bags may be checked by Customs Officers.
I-Spy for 5

← Customs
← Way out

Outside the airport buildings once again, there are plenty of things to I-Spy . . .

Here is an airport control tower. From a building like this, air traffic controllers manage all the aircraft flying into and leaving the airport. At a busy airport it is a very complicated business. . .
I-Spy for 10

. . . but the controllers have radar and other electronic aids to help them.
I-Spy for 10

Here's an aeroplane just taking off.
I-Spy for 10

35

You will find plenty of other specialized vehicles in and around an airport complex. Here is a selection. *I-Spy 5 for each of five.*

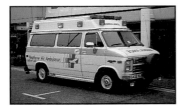

Here are the leading airlines that use British airports and which can be recognized by their tailfin insignias. Wherever two airlines share the same insignia, only one tailfin is included but both names are given. As you Spy each tailfin, score **5**.

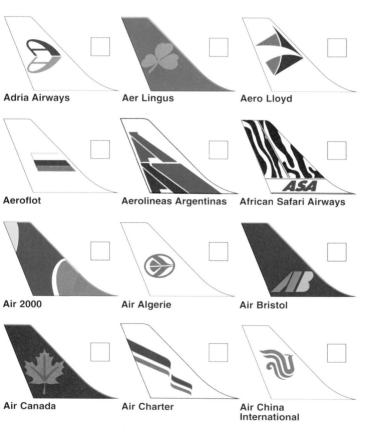

Adria Airways

Aer Lingus

Aero Lloyd

Aeroflot

Aerolineas Argentinas

African Safari Airways

Air 2000

Air Algerie

Air Bristol

Air Canada

Air Charter

Air China International

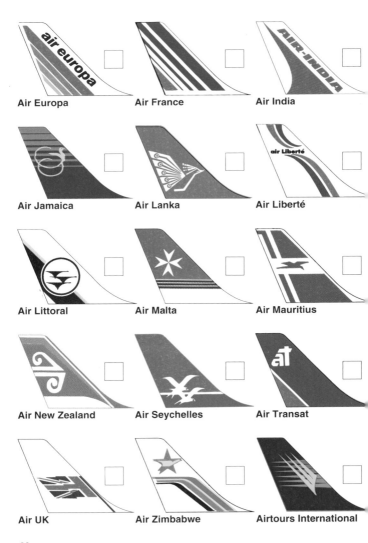

Air Europa

Air France

Air India

Air Jamaica

Air Lanka

Air Liberté

Air Littoral

Air Malta

Air Mauritius

Air New Zealand

Air Seychelles

Air Transat

Air UK

Air Zimbabwe

Airtours International

Airworld

Alitalia

Alyemen

American Airlines

American Trans Air

AOM French Airlines

Arkia Israeli Airlines

Atlantic Airways

Aurigny Air Services

Austrian Airlines

Aviaco

Balkan Bulgarian Airlines

Biman Bangladesh Airlines

Braathens Safe

 □
Brit Air

 □
Britannia Airways

 □ □ □ □
British Airways ✳

 □
British Meditteranean

 □
British Midland

 □
British World

 □
Business Air

 □
BWIA International

 □
Caledonian Airways

 □
Canadian Airlines International

 □
Cathay Pacific

 □
Channel Express

 □
China Airlines

 □
Condor Flugdienst

 □
Continental Airlines

✳ To demonstrate its position as a worldwide airline BA has devised a growing range of tailfin insignias. I-Spy 5 for each of four.

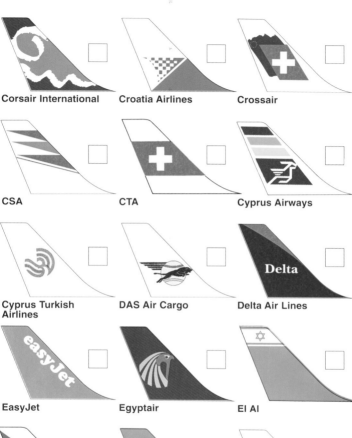

Corsair International

Croatia Airlines

Crossair

CSA

CTA

Cyprus Airways

Cyprus Turkish Airlines

DAS Air Cargo

Delta Air Lines

EasyJet

Egyptair

El Al

Emirates

Estonian Air

Ethiopian Airlines

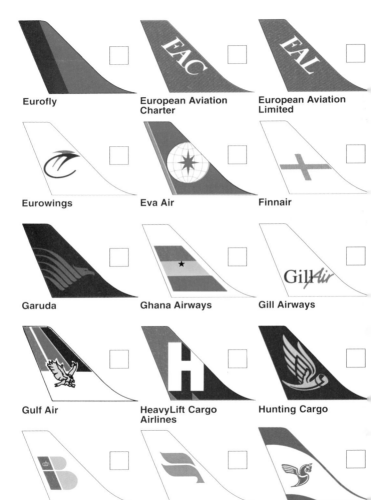

Eurofly

European Aviation Charter

European Aviation Limited

Eurowings

Eva Air

Finnair

Garuda

Ghana Airways

Gill Air

Gulf Air

HeavyLift Cargo Airlines

Hunting Cargo

Iberia

Icelandair

Iran Air

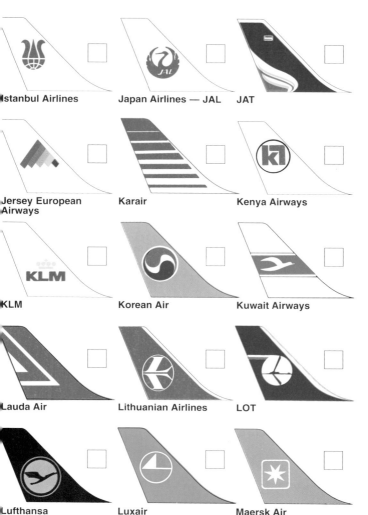

Istanbul Airlines

Japan Airlines — JAL

JAT

Jersey European Airways

Karair

Kenya Airways

KLM

Korean Air

Kuwait Airways

Lauda Air

Lithuanian Airlines

LOT

Lufthansa

Luxair

Maersk Air

Malaysia Airlines **Malév Hungarian Airlines** **Malmö**

Manx Airlines **Martinair Holland** **MEA — Middle East Airlines**

Meridiana **Monarch Airlines** **Nigeria Airways**

Northwest Airlines **Oasis International Airlines** **Olympic Airways**

Pakistan International Airlines **Philippine Air Lines — PAL** **Premiair**

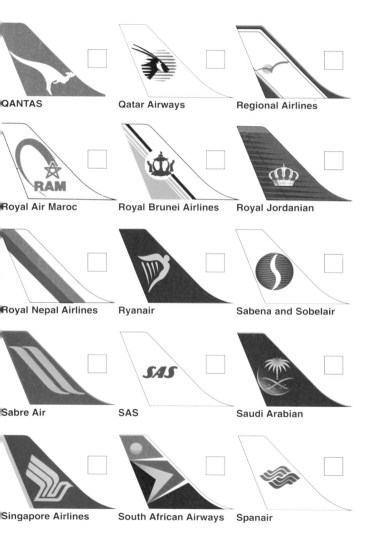

QANTAS

Qatar Airways

Regional Airlines

Royal Air Maroc

Royal Brunei Airlines

Royal Jordanian

Royal Nepal Airlines

Ryanair

Sabena and Sobelair

Sabre Air

SAS

Saudi Arabian

Singapore Airlines

South African Airways

Spanair

45

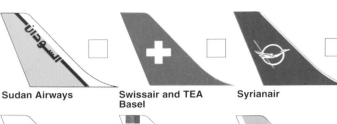

Sudan Airways

Swissair and TEA Basel

Syrianair

TAP — Air Portugal

Tarom Romanian Air Transport

TAT

Thai International

TNT International and Air Foyle

Trans World Airlines

Transaero Airlines

Transavia Airlines

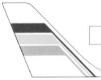

Transwede Airways

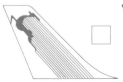

Tunis Air

TUR European Airways

Turkish Airlines

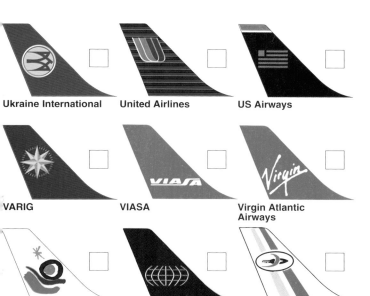

Ukraine International   **United Airlines**   **US Airways**

VARIG   **VIASA**   **Virgin Atlantic Airways**

Viva Air   **World Airways**   **Yemenia**

INDEX

Answers

What does this sign indicate: facilities for the disabled. Languageless sign: Travel pack: in a men's toilet area. baby care room: VIP: Very Important Person.

© I-Spy Limited 1997

ISBN (paperback) 1 85671 162 5

Michelin Tyre Public Limited Company
Edward Hyde Building, 38 Clarendon Road, Watford, Herts WD1 1SX

MICHELIN and the Michelin Man are Registered Trademarks of Michelin

A CIP record for this title is available from the British Library.

Edited by Neil Curtis. Designed by Richard Garratt.

The Publisher gratefully acknowledges the contribution of Richard Garratt who provided the majority of the photographs in this I-Spy book. Additional photographs are by Peter Greenland and Heathrow Airport Limited. The Publisher also wishes to thank the following for their co-operation and assistance during the preparation of this I-Spy book: BAA; Heathrow Airport Limited; Wackenhut UK Limited; Stanstead Airport Limited; Gatwick Airport Limited; and the airlines who kindly allowed photographs to be taken.

Colour reproduction by Anglia Colour.

Printed in Spain by Graficromo.